THE POETRY GAMES

LONDON AND ESSEX

Edited By Megan Roberts

First published in Great Britain in 2018 by:

Young Writers
Remus House
Coltsfoot Drive
Peterborough
PE2 9BF
Telephone: 01733 890066
Website: www.youngwriters.co.uk

FOREWORD

Since 1991 our aim here at Young Writers has been to encourage creativity in children and to inspire a love of the written word. Each competition is tailored to the relevant age group, hopefully giving each pupil the inspiration and incentive to create their own piece of creative writing, whether it's a poem or a short story. We truly believe that seeing their work in print gives students a sense of achievement and pride.

For our latest contest The Poetry Games, secondary school pupils were given the challenge to stand up for what they believe in using nothing but the power of the pen. Using poetry as their tool, these aspiring poets were given the opportunity to express their thoughts and feelings on the topics that matter to them through verse. Using a variety of themes and styles, these featured poets leave a lasting impression of their inner thoughts and feelings, making this anthology a rare insight into the next generation.

We encourage young writers to express themselves and address topics that matter to them, which sometimes means exploring sensitive or difficult topics. If you have been affected by any issues raised in this book, details on where to find help can be found at: **www.youngwriters.co.uk/support.**

CONTENTS

Independent Entries

Iris Mary Dongwe   1
Gabija Valatkaite (14)   2
Rachael Maya Moraise (16)   8
Sharwyn Gordon   11
Reena Robinson (11)   12
Yusra Mohamed (12)   14
Atifa Dukanwala (14)   16
Ella Patriciarose Beschizza (13)   18
Keira Louise Hayward (12)   19
Jade Athwal-McNair (18)   20
Jelani Cecil Eguakun (14)   22
Falhat Mohamud (12)   24
Yasameen Rahimi (15)   25
Niamh Walters (14)   26
Leah Prescott   28
Ajani Samuel Eguakun (11)   29

Alexandra Park School, Haringey

Rosie Solomons (12)   30
Lucie Weston (11)   32

Arts & Media School, Islington

Ilwad Roble (12)   34
Sabrina Rage (12)   36
Dylan Brown (12)   37

Bow School, Bow

Taylor Jenevieve Roberts (12)   38

Fine Arts College Hampstead, London

Rory Price Phillips (15)   39
Stella Johnston (14)   41
Yasmin Bligh-Hasan (16)   43

Greenwich Free School, London

Jade Bliss (13)   46

HAFS Academy, Stratford

Sheikh Mahdi Islam (14)   47
Jamal Ahsan Mian (13)   48
Mohammed Ajwad Uddin (12)   50
Ahmad Yusuf Patel (12)   52
Usman Iqbal (13)   54
Abdullah Anwar (14)   56
Adil Iqbal (14)   58
Rayhan Talukder (13)   60
Thamim Islam (14)   62
Huzaifa Mujahid Ali (13)   63
Hamid Alom (13)   64
Enis Koesem (12)   65

Italia Conti Academy Of Theatre Arts, Islington

Emma Moore (12)   66

Lady Margaret School, London

Ruby Da Cruz Heale (12)   67
Maddy Kidd-May (12)   68

London Enterprise Academy, London

Saber Kilwa	70
Ashif Hussain	72
Isa Abdussalam	73

Morpeth School, London

Sayeeda Islam (13)	74
Shahara Ajmir (13)	76
Alisha Islam (12)	78
Amir Hamza (13)	79
Fahmeda Azad (13)	80

Plashet School, East Ham

Tasneem Mulla (13)	81
Muna Elmi (14)	82
Alaina Siddiqui (12)	85
Norin Khatun (13)	86
Ashwina Kalanathan (14)	88
Nazifa Islam (14)	89
Humaira Khondkar (14)	90

Rickmansworth School, Rickmansworth

Alessio Capozzi	91

St Saviour's And St Olave's School, Southwark

Mahrou Marjan Meem (13)	92
Deborah Esan (15)	95
Elle Simmonds (12)	96
Grace Webb (12)	97
Hannah Lin (12)	98
Nasrin Kasim (12)	99
Romesa Kashif (13)	100
Raima Kashif (11)	102
Mary Konadu (13)	104
Teniola Oduala (12)	105
Akonte Tyger (12)	106
Tabitha O'Callaghan (12)	107

Elsie McDowell (13)	108
Temi Odukale (12)	110
Lilyana Baird-Thomas (11)	111
Tosin Agoro (12)	112

St Thomas More High School For Boys, Westcliff-On-Sea

Finn Parker (13)	113
Charlie Betts (14)	114
Paddy-Joe Brandon-Blatch (14)	116
Anthony Otuorimuo (13)	118
Luke Randall (13)	120
Heshan Mahendra (13)	122
Lemuel Munyaradzi Bultman (13)	124
Oliver Stanton (14)	126
Henry Tilley (13)	128
Aaran Wingrove-Smith (13)	130
Leo Palmer (14)	132
Stefan Protic (14)	133
Omotade Adekunle Atobatele (13)	134
George Sandell (12)	135
Sean David (13)	136
Areeb Khan (12)	137
Freddie Treacher (14)	138
Zachary Sossou (14)	140
Luca Apicella (13)	142
Luca Butteriss (14)	144
Will Hood (14)	145
William Seymour (12)	146
Alfie Williams (14)	148
Olly Robinson (13)	149
Milan Jomon (14)	150
George Standley (12)	151
Harvey Hysop (13)	152
Sonny Palmer (13)	153
Sotirios Sotiras (15)	154
M J Bowden (14)	156
Bartosz Szech (14)	157
Thomas Miller (14)	158
Rio Abloh (14)	159
Luke Bowden (12)	160

Alfie Wilsmore (12)	161
Ernest Aquino (13)	162
Matthew Wills Vandervelden (14)	163
Jude Peach (13)	164
Tom Cozens (12)	165
Connor Thomas John Lee (14)	166
Efeose Christopher Ukegheson (13)	167
Gio De Belen (14)	168
Joshua Naish (13)	169
Alfie Glover (13)	170
Aaron Antony (14)	171
Zak Crisp (13)	172
William Peck (13)	173
Charlie Mchugh (14)	174
Korede Obayanju-Oladoyinbo (14)	175
Vinay John Anthony Soares (13)	176
Harrison James Baker (13)	177

The Ellen Wilkinson School For Girls, Acton

Touleen Elawi (14)	178
Najah Harir (16)	179
Son Gyong Kim (14)	180

LACK AND GAIN OF FREEDOM

Back in the olden days, not many countries had freedom.
To this day, some still don't have enough or any at all.
There are many types of freedom
And actually most schools in Britain lack at least one of
these types:
This is freedom of individuality.
Schools do not allow us to express ourselves unless it is for
charity or an after-school event.
They do this by making us look like one another.
School is not the only place where you don't get as much
freedom as you like.
Parents don't trust us kids to stay home alone,
So they work shorter hours to just to watch us?
We don't even have the freedom to watch the different
kinds of movies we'd like to watch, such as 12 and 15
movies.
But this is just a way of discipline nowadays.
Our parents, teachers, deputies and head teachers are
trying to make us the best we can be,
They want us to believe, achieve and succeed.
Yes, in some areas we still have to fight for freedom, such as
freedom of speech and race.
But the freedom which the adults in our lives are not giving
us we should be thankful,
They are constantly working to make our generation great!

Iris Mary Dongwe

OUR COMPLEX WORLD

We live in a complex world, but what makes it so complex? Oddly enough, the answer has been right under our noses this entire time, but we, humans, aren't prepared to face the 'truth';
we are in denial.

We say that the world has been complex ever since the beginning of time, ever since its existence was first uncovered from the breached blanket of stars and darkness we call the universe,
yet humanity has always found a way to smother the truth with its naive and recalcitrant mindset, which ceaselessly has the inability to embrace reality with open arms and can only, instead, create a fake facade to brainwash people into thinking it's the world's fault for their sufferings.

No matter what facts are thrown in your direction, it's crystal clear to see that, because of our greed, our lust for power, our lack of avidity towards others around us, we humans decided to declare the world as complex.

Not only do we have a complex world, but we also have a complex galaxy. A tremendous galaxy which, as we speak, is extending to the point where the sun's savage flames could no longer ration its warmth with it.

The universe is never-ending, full of mystery.

It expands into the dark abyss only to be greeted by total isolation and eerie silence for the rest of eternity.

Sadly, we do not care much for this fascinating cosmos of ours that holds several secrets and discoveries yet to be made.
Instead, we are only attentive to the materialistic commodities our globe has to offer.

I am one of those seven billion humans
Inhabiting the planet called Earth.
I am a frail, small speck of dust compared to the nations of beings cohabiting on the vast patches of land, surrounded by seawater known as continents.

I do not have much to offer.
I cannot offer a sanctuary nor a safe haven for you to hide in and feel secure within,
I cannot harbour the world's irreversible damage and problems,
I cannot do much, yet I have a voice.

Though this voice of mine is small and unappealing to many, it has words of wisdom, words that could one day change the world.

Declaring the world as complex was simply a way to source the long-awaited satisfaction and purpose the deprived men and women of this Earth have desperately been longing for. These men and women slave their deteriorating bodies day in and day out, to provide for their families, to survive, to one day find out that the hardships they went through and the prices they had to pay were going to bring about good and reward them later in life.

As everybody who's inhabiting this world knows, nothing in our malicious world can be obtained for free without sacrifice.
These people sacrifice their existence every day, day in and out, only to ironically get up and do it all over again the next day.
They obliviously do this for years on end because they know that this is the only way to survive in this hellish world and to show that they are living proof to others that there will never be an avail for change.

Change is what is really needed.
Change is what will truly allow the current suffering generation to finally breathe a sigh of relief and have them continue to saunter this land until they are faced with the fated doors of death.
This 'change' is what will encourage them to pass through those tabooed doors without hesitation, without feeling regret, without feeling like they have left the people they love behind to experience the same cruel life they once did.

They won't feel this because change finally happened, because change was able to provide help for their descendants,
The future of mankind.

Change is what is wanted, but change is hard to get.

People come from different places all over the globe and all these people also have a unique voice which cannot be ignored.

They may have this voice however not all of these 'unique voices' should necessarily be heard and be taken into account.
Why?
Because they do not all compensate an understanding, they do not compensate an understanding of what they are truly getting themselves into nor are they fully aware of the effects those hypothetical words they are spouting to the public have on the world.

They do not know the future, they do not know what circumstances the world will be in ten years time.
They do not know and that is why those individuals who do know the extent of their actions are afraid to step up and take charge of the situation.

They don't want to have a burden on their shoulders,
They do not want to have any regrets.
That, of course, is understandable,
But if they won't stand, who will?

Who will secure your kin's future?
Who will secure your future?
Who will try and fail to get results?
All these answers are unknown,
But the first steps are all in front of our eyes.
What are our main problems,
What is making us suffer as a whole?

Is it climate change?

Lack of human rights?
Lack of animal rights?
Lack of education?
Lack of understanding?
Lack of acceptance?
Lack of compassion?
Lack of clean water?
Lack of agriculture and farming?
Lack of generosity and kindness?

The list of possibilities can go on and on,
But as long as humans can recognise that things need to be
done to improve their situation as well as others,
It shows they still have morals and they still do have some
selflessness inside of them.
Once everybody understands this crucial life lesson, it will
eliminate the greed coming from within their tainted hearts
and it will show that a huge step of improvement has been
made to save humanity from its current and upcoming
state.

This teaching can continue to progress even further until it
can officially be known as the biggest leap to successfully
save humanity and the globe's inhabitants.
This revolutionary change will begin when you begin.

You can begin by completing small actions, such as turning
those flickering lights off in your kitchen, bedroom,
bathroom, every room within your house earlier rather than
keeping them on for long periods of time to just waste
energy.

You can also be saving our planet by recycling your food and waste products such as plastic, paper and glass bottles.

Remember, small changes can become big changes.

Congratulations, five years down the line, you've managed to, with all the other nations around the world:
Prevent further climate change, air pollution, animal abuse and several other serious matters that have been endangering our world for over a millennium.

Congratulations, you've saved yourself,
The world and the people you love.
You've managed to create a better world with less problems, less reason for greed, less reason to long for materialistic objects and instead, you've made people long for family instead of urging them to toss them aside for independence and selfish reasons such as fame and money.
Doesn't this give humanity fewer and fewer reasons to label the world as complex?
Do you still think that the source of your problems is because the world is so complex?

Like I said, like this small, frail piece of dust said, we humans are too naive to change and accept that we are the source of our own suffrage.
We make the world complex and we blame it on none other but our own precious human race.

Now, after everything you've heard,
Do you still think the world is complex?

Gabija Valatkaite (14)

POETRY: MY COPING MECHANISM

Poetry. It's like a painkiller,
My own personal coping mechanism.
Little pieces of my heart, poured out in literary form,
But I love it.
All my emotions, my innermost thoughts and feelings
Laid out for me to see
And, when I look back at it, my heart swells with pride.
I did that.

It's my one true love, my passion.
It's not for everyone, but it's perfectly me.
Perfectly Rachael.
It's all I've ever known.
My oxygen,
I live it, breathe it.
Nobody can take it away from me, because it's mine.
I desperately hang onto it, afraid to let it go.

It's incredible how words on a page can convey how you feel inside,
No need to speak, just pour your heart out on the page.
The rest will come.

Words are my safe haven, I hide behind them
Because they express who I truly am,

They shelter me, comfort me,
Protect me.

Poetry is where I'm at home, I can be me.
I can write what I please, with nobody to judge me.
No teachers to suggest how I should 'add in more imagery'
Or maybe a sprinkle of 'descriptive language'
And a dash of 'sophisticated vocabulary'.

They try to get me to change the very thing that makes me
me.
How I write reflects who I am, breaking the moulds,
Defying the status quo.
When you think 'teenage girl',
I know for a fact that poetry isn't the first thing that springs
to mind,
But, if you don't accept it, you don't accept me.

Flashes of inspiration, of pure brilliance, I live for it.
I live for the thrill, creative juices flowing from my head,
To my heart, to my fingertips.
Electrifying, magnificent.

Until it's all over, my exhilaration vanishes
And I'm dragged back down to an unfortunate reality.
My head's no longer in the clouds,
I'm no longer living in a fantasy world,
No longer cooped up in my own writing cave,

As a professional poet with fruit tea in hand,
But ordinary Rachael, in a mundane, boring, ordinary world.

Rachael Maya Moraise (16)

WHAT I BELIEVE IN

Some people believe in what they can touch and what they can see,
What do I believe in?
I believe in the amazing,
Beyond the limits a naked eye can reach.

Some people believe in every word spoken by their friends,
What do I believe in?
I believe in me, sometimes words have deceptive ends.

There are some who believe in the words of those that they aspire to be,
What do I believe in?
I believe in ingenuity and a questioning mentality.

There are some who believe in playing the role in life that you already have,
What do I believe in?
I believe in working so hard to earn that role you want so bad.

I believe in myself, I believe in my family and friends,
I believe that if I work so hard nothing can stop me until my end,
I believe in the people I surround myself with,
The people I love, the people I cherish,
I believe in you and me
And I believe that there is enough love and goodness for everybody.

Sharwyn Gordon

THE BOY WHO NEVER GAVE UP

Inspired by My Hero Academia

At a young age, he realised
Not all men are born equal.

People develop their superpower at the age of four,
But he never got his 'quirk' and was seen as worthless.
"Look at my quirk, I shoot water from my hands."
"Look at my quirk, it's amazing."
"What's your quirk?"
"Don't have one."
That didn't stop him from trying to become what he wanted
to be.
Even though he didn't have what everyone else had,
He never gave up.

Even though everyone was doubting him.
He never gave up.

Even though everyone told him he couldn't do it,
He still never gave up.
He met the man that inspired him
But he told him that he couldn't do it.
He did go down,
But he picked himself back up.
He was worthy to have a quirk,

He tried as best as he could.
So it was given to him.

Now free to complete the dream he worked to achieve.
What you put effort in with your heart and soul,
What you worked for will come out.
No matter how difficult or how hard it is,
Or if no one has ever done it before.
Just know that you can do it.

Reena Robinson (11)

IS HAPPINESS WADS OF GREEN?

I have always wondered
This very thought would ponder as I slept
Why can't everyone be happy?
Why must people be unhappy?
Or if they should be happy, why not?
Why must people live their lives in misery and put up with it?
Why must people sleep in the finest of silks
And the fluffiest of pillows
And the unfortunate others sleep with rags rather than riches?
We all wonder.

Those who are rich may have gold,
But very few have a heart brimming with gold.
These very few are hard to find,
But those who have a heart of gold but have rags not riches.
Those of which destiny has chosen their lives as such,
Those who put humanity before wads of green.
Surely those are the people who should be recognised, but only few are seen.

Ponder this as you sleep at night,
Think of those who would happily live life
And think are wads of green the answer to happiness?

Or is it having the world full of good deeds?
Surely humanity knows what happiness is,
It can be sitting with your family,
Or eating some ice cream.
But your only source of happiness
Should not be wads of green.

Yusra Mohamed (12)

THE REMINISCENCE OF A ROSE

The single flower that's so impossible to hate;
fragile and elegant,
even when it stops blooming.

Your words could calm
even the most chaotic oceans,
always soothing, rarely wavering,
with soft notes of comfort.
My brain has not yet learned your speech,
but my heart has memorised your music
and pen.

Even your eyes could mesmerise
the most soulless creature.
Your sweet face leaves people dreaming in heartache.
Beautiful from every angle;
prickling, irreplaceable.

I admire your patience a lot,
it provides serenity to fiery spirits;
a light that you possess,
that you should not allow to be burned out
by anyone else.
There aren't enough words my brain knows
to describe you,

but my heart knows you better.

The boundary has been surpassed
and I am met with an empty canvas.
For how can I create art,
when you are the *art*?

Atifa Dukanwala (14)

HE

He was colour-blind to the rainbow that this world is,
Day by day walking amongst the invisible beauty,
Holding onto his long-gone hope,
Deteriorating and desynchronising slowly,
In his head was nothing but black and grey,
What was green again, red or blue?

The night sky flowed above him and the stars watched
As his melancholy movement filled the void
Of elaborate nothingness
That created this beige world,

Each and every one of us,
A time spender, moving along in obscure repeated motion,
Just to soon disintegrate and never be remembered.

His idea of love was a painful ephemeral nemesis,
Born to appeal the most broken of minds.
Many of these people shall not endure in such a loneliness
he felt, why in all means,
In which case would one decide to trust in one another;
To give them their fragile heart and have them handle it for
God's sake.

Ella Patriciarose Beschizza (13)

18

BULLYING

Bullying is like a ghost that follows you around wherever you go.
It is a torture and pain that can scar you for life.
Why do people do it, why do they bother?
It could be physical or verbal or cyber or at school,
But either way, it's still a living nightmare.
Even if you are tall, short, fat or skinny, stand out, be bold, be you,
Because you are beautiful.
Bullies can seek you out when you expect it or not,
They are parasitic people, who suck the life out of you,
They are all heartless inside.
Selfishness is a failure but your happiness is a success,
Bullying can be manifest in many ways,
The victim could begin to internalise all of the negative feelings
That the unwanted attention evokes.

Keira Louise Hayward (12)

AQUA ICE AND WHITE SNOW

A land of pure ice,
Nothing else within sight.
A combination of blue and white,
To represent the light.
Caverns and castles sculpted with ice as their main device.
During the night, the reflection of the moon's light,
Reveals the magic and beauty it holds.

A natural beauty of the world,
Made of ice and shimmering snow.
Frozen flurries floating from the sky above.
Gleaming coloured Northern Lights that are always loved.
Glistening aqua ice,
Wondrous to behold.
Snowflakes are unique,
Hidden like treasure,
Like pieces of precious gold.

The swirling storms,
Turning hot into cold,
Water into snow.
The frozen ocean once with fresh flowing water,
Now resembles shards of glass and snow.
Magnificent mountains,

A breath-taking view,
Awaits only a few.
It has never been seen before.
The magic and beauty foretold.

Jade Athwal-McNair (18)

LIVES NOT KNIVES!

While the poor boy lies there,
For more than you can bear.
And when you're just there to stare,
Although you may not care,
A life has gone, it can never be repaid.

The mother in agony,
The father in despair.
The feeling of losing a loved one,
Is really quite not there.

Stephen Lawrence,
Damilola Taylor,
Gone because of knives.
A piece of cutlery that took their lives.
You can't be thinking
Leaving lives sinking,
Make the change, drop the knives.

This is an issue,
The pain and agony leaving tissues.
Carrying a knife does not make you cool,
It really just makes you a fool.

It's lives not knives,
That's the drill,
For there is no pill,

So please chill
And drop the knives.

Jelani Cecil Eguakun (14)

I STAND BEFORE YOU

I stand before you and await my trial.
Are you offended because of my style?
What do you see: the scarf or the girl?
While you debate, shall I give you a twirl?

You call it 'rag', a sign of oppression.
You demand to ban it, a sign of aggression.
Your concern is noted, firmly turned down.
We are Muslims, this hijab's our crown.

Who are these people who kill in His name?
Threaten us and demand we do the same?
They say they're Muslims, I say they're liars.
Murder and evil: both signs of the Fire.

I pray to you God: show me the way.
I may wear it right, but I have gone astray.
Hours have gone, there's no going back.
As for my future, the prospect seems black.

Falhat Mohamud (12)

ME!

Yes, I am a child.
I can be strong and I can be weak,
I can be judged and I can judge,
I can do this and I can do that.
Been through the pain
Again and again,
So, don't judge me by what you see,
What you hear and my mistakes.
At the end I am the one who's been through it all.
I can be a nerd,
I can be a geek,
I can be bullied and I can be the bully,
But I know there are people out there for me.
For the best and for the worst,
At the end I am still me.

Yasameen Rahimi (15)

THE LAMP IN THE MIRROR

Time again, I try to wait
For tears that do not come
And all my sorrows fade away with the tide.
I wait patiently for the desolation,
The inhale before the gasp.
Time and time again,
I watch my life fall away,
Wondering how I could have lost
So much.
My medieval dreams
Still bleeding
In my broken hand.
But time again I hold my head high
And say it will be the last time,
I say it will be the last time.
Can you help me dear God?
Help me to find the way,
Help me to find the way.
For I don't.
Know.
The way.
Let this be the last time.
Let this please be the last time.

Please.
Oh please.
The last time.

Niamh Walters (14)

CHRISTMAS

Happy holiday season a time to give.
All the team give their best to help pack hampers for those
in need.
Meeting new people when you deliver to their door.
Presents inside the bag for the children,
Things they might not have had before.
Everything we do to help gets better and better.
Rich or poor, we still care about them all.
Season had ended for hampers this year,
Until next year when we meet again.

Leah Prescott

FOLLOW YOUR BELIEFS

When black people were not treated right,
He stood strong to lead the fight.
He fought with words, not guns or darts,
He changed people's minds and hearts.
Martin Luther King's life has passed,
But his dreams are free at last.

Ajani Samuel Eguakun (11)

EVER NOTICED

Have you ever noticed
The dance of the trees,
That wave high and low
In the autumn breeze?

The pink blossoms
That fall with the leaves,
That colour the concrete
And make some sneeze.

The ducks that swim
And the birds that sing,
The colours that travel
From wing to wing.

The stars that shine
Through your windows at night,
And lead the way
To the morning light.

Have you ever noticed
That at the end of each day,
There is more and more plastic
Afloat in the bay.

There is less land
And less trees,

More toxic fumes
And a thicker breeze.

Man is oblivious
To the mess it's made,
As long as it's rich,
As long as it's paid.

Look what we've done
Created a war,
Hacked the Earth
Down to its core.

So I say, "Stop!
Continue no more.
We may be rich,
But the Earth is now poor."

We mustn't proceed
In these pointless fights,
For we aren't the only ones
Who deserve rights.

Rosie Solomons (12)
Alexandra Park School, Haringey

MOTHER, WILL I EVER SEE YOU AGAIN?

Love.
A simple word.
A word to change life
Like a never-ending harp, twinkling beneath the stars.
You are my everything,
A pure, delicate silhouette in the distance.
Able to melt the sunset into a burst of colours
of unimaginable beauty.
Able to make the words of my mouth
Repeat over and over again with one word:
Love. Love. Love.
Help me conquer this beast
Emerging from the depths of my heart,
Turning my whole body aflame
With your smile,
With your eyes,
With your everything.
My heart is a frail grain of sand,
Being swept up by monstrous waves of fear of the unknown.
Will I come back to life?
Because you are the light that guides me in the dark
And I long to envelop you in my arms,
So let me hold onto you

One last time,
Before my life plunges into darkness.
Mother, will I ever see you again?

Lucie Weston (11)
Alexandra Park School, Haringey

HOW COULD YOU?

Islamophobes, Islamophobes,
This poem is for you.
Listen up, don't ignore,
'Cause this poem *is* the truth.

You rebel against our religion,
You think we don't deserve a position,
You think I can't achieve my future visions.
How could you?

You look at me and call me 'oppressed',
Simply because of how I dress.
I never knew what I wear could affect you.
You just always seem to judge me,
By the clothing I wear with pride.
How could you?

Your hatred will never drive me away,
You will always find me to be the same person I am today.
Why do you always want to beat me down?
Why do you always want to make *my* life difficult?
How could you?

Okay, fine, let the news claim us as 'terrorists',
Maybe it's about time *you* saw a therapist.
Listen to all the dreadful news the media has to say about
us,
You just don't seem to have a lot of faith and trust.

How could you?

You glare at me,
Hoping that it'll blaze into my heart.
You try emotionally breaking into me,
Hoping it'll get into me.
How could you?

Haters are all the same,
They all looking for some kind of fame.
And it's such a shame,
That haters will *always* hate.

Ilwad Roble (12)
Arts & Media School, Islington

I TRUSTED YOU

I thought I could trust you,
I thought I could come to you.
I thought you were the solution to my problems,
The answer to my questions,
Or the tissues to my issues.
But no, you're not.

Only a few have the gift of trust,
Many haven't received the gift of faith.

I am someone,
Yet they think I am the dumb one.
Don't you realise that I am here if you need someone who you can trust?

Trust firm belief in the reliability, truth or ability of someone or something.

Sabrina Rage (12)
Arts & Media School, Islington

DO NOT REPEAT

Eat, sleep, wake, repeat,
There's more to life than that.
People are here and people are there
And you're still lying around.
People work, people train
And people don't give up
And you're still lying around.
People die and people are born,
But you're still alive, so enjoy it.

Dylan Brown (12)
Arts & Media School, Islington

TRUTH AND LIES

My voice is silent, unheard, swept away,
People say to me, "Just try another day."
Most give up fighting for their voice,
For their chance to make their choice,
To be known, to shine with the stars,
To feel normal, not like I live on Mars.
But, maybe I should just be myself,
I don't want to be someone else.
I'm confused, who should I believe?
Who is telling the truth and who deceives?
Where is the truth?
Where are the lies?
Are they hiding hate beneath blank eyes?
What do I do now I'm here?
I wish the answers were more clear.

Taylor Jenevieve Roberts (12)
Bow School, Bow

GOING TO WAR

Going to war,
I would feel sick,
Knowing a bayonet
Would be as familiar as a stick.
Killing every German
That I could see,
Even though they're obliged to fight,
Just like me.
Call me a coward,
Call me afraid,
But I wouldn't fight,
Even if I was paid.
I don't care what you say,
I don't care how you speak,
Because killing someone like him,
Would be killing someone like me.
It wouldn't make sense,
There's no wonder they call it self defence.
How can you ask for help,
When we'll die too?
And all the posters say
'I want you'.
It's true, I do,
I love my country,
But half my country's going to die,

Going to a war where you lied.
Not telling them that their children and wives would cry,
Nor telling them they'd die when they applied.
Telling them this war was a game, a fun ride,
When you were trying to cover up suicide.
You told them they'd be alright,
You told them to fight
And you made it seem like
They'd be home for toast and marmite.
General Haig, what have you done?
Killed thousands of humans on day one.
Thousands of humans lying dead on the floor,
This is the product of war.

Rory Price Phillips (15)
Fine Arts College Hampstead, London

INSPIRED IMAGINATION

It's creativity,
It's deniability
Of impossibility,
In an actuality.

Deny reality,
Embrace clarity.
Use your ability,
To start your own activity.

Pick up a pen,
Pick up a rifle.
Click the top,
Click the magazine.

Run, be active,
Jump, just fly.
I respect those who do more
Than those who just try.

This world is built on inspiration.
A human nation, a feat of nature,
A creature of our mind's features,
To make our own future.

If you can't stop,
Don't stop.
Do stop stopping.

Creativity is a gift to me,
Mandela preaching vitality.
The reality is mortality,
Our mortalities make us.

Instead of reading the book,
Obeying the book,
Abiding and minding the book.
Rewrite it.

Do you think Einstein didn't try
Minding his mind
And creating without creativity?
No,
Einstein was inspired by inspiration,
Obama created for his creation,
Victoria nationalised a nation.
So you think you can create without creation?
Imagine first before your imagination.

I respect, inspire, love and adore,
All emotions I feel to imagine and more.
Imagination created so we could do the creating,
Be inspired to make the inspiration.
It's imagination.

Stella Johnston (14)
Fine Arts College Hampstead, London

CAPABILITY

Maybe, once in a while,
We need a push in the wrong direction
Not to hinder ourselves,
But to correct our perfection.
Sometimes we question our beliefs when we say 'amen'
So how many times in a year
Can we say that we rose up again?
How can we rise up if we never had something to rise up to?
Why be so dependant on the external
To find your own gratitude,
When you can find that you can be your own motivation
In the midst of the heart which solely belongs to you
But, sometimes belief loses itself in a constant,
Counting people through a wave of sudden hinderance to
your path
From an unexpected series of events.
What if this life is to allow you to embrace what you love to
do?
Because, as long as you are able to breathe,
There's always a second chance in front of you.
How do you know that the reality you experience is the
truest reality of all?
Because in this world, there are another seven billion
realities completely different to yours.
So, trusting your heart will enable you
To unlock that mental key you have been looking to find in
something other than yourself.

But now you know that you already have everything you need within you,
Don't let things stop you from pursuing the new -
The things that come from the inevitability of being alive.
Rise above all the 'screw yous'
And keep your focus on to the thing you love most,
Because that is what we are all guided to do.
These words are a wake-up call from your spirit to your brain,
To shake you awake through the muddle of knowledge you're trying to get through.
Take a long and deep breath to refresh your memory of who you are,
And who you were before all the negativity got to you.
Who you were when you first opened your wide eyes
And viewed the beautiful and compassionate universe,
Inside your mother's eyes for the first time
And just knew that, within your soul, you will always contain her protection.
And through that, you could dream anything you wanted
And fully be believed and knew that she would always be there in the middle of the cold night to soothe you.
That is how you knew you could reach for anything.
And, if it wasn't right, she would do her best to teach you,
Because now you have the sacred capability within you that allows you to strive forward
And reach your desires without a care in the world.
As you possess a true calling from your inner self

That can finally draw open the curtains to let you know
It is time for a change and a time to go through a
tremendous transformation
Into becoming the best version of yourself that there ever
could be.
Because you will always know that your soul will piece itself
together in time
And perfect your life for your own good.
And, truthfully, that means striving to learn from that
sudden hinderance in the wrong direction.

Yasmin Bligh-Hasan (16)

Fine Arts College Hampstead, London

JUST PLAIN ME

That feeling you get in your chest
And all you want to do
Is remind them that they are the best.
You think that you know them,
But you knew nothing at all
And when they don't feel the same,
You start to bawl.
You find someone else
And they're cool,
But all you worry about is if you're acting like a fool.
You feel so happy that they have chosen you,
But, you know sometimes it ends
And you really feel blue.
All you can think about is:
I care about them,
I want to hug them,
I want them to know how I feel.
I still want them to be mine.
But the strongest thought of all:
Did it mean anything to them?

Jade Bliss (13)
Greenwich Free School, London

FROM THE WOMB TO THE TOMB

From the start, we had a connection,
Although my heart had not formed.
As the years went by, my love for you
Grew stronger and transformed.

You've struggled so much for me,
I know I can never repay my debt.
Even if I was to take you all around the world
In a golden jet.

Forgive me for all the fights that we've had,
All the rubbish on the messy floors
And the clothes that went back into their drawers
And all the pain you had to endure because of me.

And I know this sounds cliché,
But you are the best.
And I hope, one day, you can be pleased with me
And can finally rest.

So forgive me, forgive me for it all,
Forgive me for growing up
As soon as you taught me how to crawl.

Since God places heaven under your feet,
I hope the gates of Heaven are where we finally meet.

Sheikh Mahdi Islam (14)
HAFS Academy, Stratford

STOP POLLUTION

Everyone has a job from the first day of our birth,
That it's important to take care of our Earth.
So, if you want to live where it's clean,
Then we all need to make it more green.

Instead of planting trees,
They are chopped down, replaced by factories.
The glaciers in the north are melting,
The climate changes and animals are dying.

So, when people dirty the river,
They don't care about it.
Stop making it worse,
Or you will die of thirst.

Beautiful and healthy creatures will not hatch
In the Amazon garbage patch.
Learn what you can do to help,
Show that you're not careless.

Or when it comes to buying a new car,
Choose a small one, it will take you just as far.
So far, there is evolution,
This is a problem, which is pollution.

So stop it before you make it worse
Or you need to suffer.

You should know all about this
If you care, so you won't make it worse.

Jamal Ahsan Mian (13)
HAFS Academy, Stratford

MOTHERS ARE WONDERS

Every morning, when I arise,
It comes to my surprise,
My mum is all ready,
Reading by the baby.
I should be grateful for I have the best of all,
Some children have none at all.

Around the table, we take a seat,
Mum serves her delicious food to eat.
I praise God for my mother,
She truly is such a wonder.
I love my mum for who she is.
When she gives me hugs and a kiss,
I close my eyes in pure bliss.

My mum is my light,
She is the one who made me bright.
I don't know where I would be without her,
She has truly given me my powers.
When times are melancholy,
She cheers me with an ice lolly.

As Mum gets older,
I must grow bigger and bolder.
The way Mum treated me when I was young

Is unrepayable.
But let me try and give back some of my love.
I can't ever repay Mum,
For she has given me everything that I want.

When I'm feeling dumb,
There she is, my dear mum.
When I'm feeling lazy,
There mum is,
Giving me love like crazy.

When Mum is feeling down,
I'm ready to take her frown
And turn it upside down.
When Mum is feeling down,
I can say one thing:
Roses are red,
Violets are blue,
You are my dearly loved mother
And I love you.

So, be grateful to your mother,
She is the light in our eyes.
Mums give us life's colour,
She takes in all our needing cries.
And that's how mothers are true wonders.

Mohammed Ajwad Uddin (12)
HAFS Academy, Stratford

PARENTS

Parents are the best thing you could have,
As they brought you into the world.
Nobody could be a better advisor to you,
Than those we call parents.

They are definitely the most valuable thing to you,
They have to work hard all day and most of the night.
Mum cleaning and Dad working,
For you, they work tirelessly for money to provide.

Since you were a baby and you were just born,
They have been going through so much trouble.
Just to provide for you a better future,
For you and your sisters or brothers.

If you have one or more siblings,
Younger or older than you,
You may think they favour them more,
But they still definitely love you equally too.

They may say things like "Turn off the TV,"
Or maybe even, "Go to sleep or no sweets tomorrow,"
But they are trying to do the best for you
And they are trying to help you in your future.

Wasn't there a time when they bought you the latest toy?
Or gave you some designer clothes you wanted?

Next time you feel angry at them,
Just try to remember those joyous moments.

So remember, parents are the best thing you could have,
As they brought you into the world.
Nobody could be a better advisor to you,
Than those we call parents.

Ahmad Yusuf Patel (12)
HAFS Academy, Stratford

MY FAMILY

I have a special family,
Who live thousands of miles away.
And, although they are so dear to me,
I cannot see them every day.

So, when Allah grants me the chance
To reunite with them again,
I begin to count the days until
I'm with people who are closer than best friends.

They shower me with gifts
And make it comfortable for me to stay.
They would put aside their needs,
Only to let me have my way.

The love they radiate to me
Would revive the most broken heart,
But that's why the pain is more difficult,
When the time comes to depart.

At that time, tissues become our company,
As tears become our screen.
While we try our best to hold on to each other,
Despite the many miles inbetween.

But this is life in its essence,
The separation and the pain.

And, once we come together,
There's laughter once again.

Thank God for such a family,
Whose love makes goodbyes so hard.
And hope for a paradise,
Where there's love without separation.

Usman Iqbal (13)
HAFS Academy, Stratford

THE RING IS RED, MY OPPONENT IS BLUE

As I pivot about the ring,
Momentarily delirious,
My arms feel detached,
Irresponsive to my command.
Oh Lord, it hurts,
Oh God, it burns.
My stomach, does it churn.

Before the ring, a frozen stare,
Leading blood to zealous fists raging.

A spar turned beating,
Out spurts blood,
Beneath the deafening roaring.

A clip to the clavicle,
My gut is somewhat hysterical.

His profile is Greek to me.

I work at his midsection
Until he invokes destruction.

Rest assured, I assure you,
I meant to hurt you.
The strike I threw,

Held intent,
To harm you.

My palm would often commemorate with your jaw.
Rest assured, incapable of defending you,
Would be the society of law.

Come what, come may,
And to what the spectators relay,
In their lofty timber,
Or woven enclosures,
They go weak at the knees.

My boxing gloves are red,
My opponent is blue.

Abdullah Anwar (14)
HAFS Academy, Stratford

THE CREATION

There's a sight that I see,
Before the sun goes down
And leaves have changed colour,
From green, but not yet brown.

Rather, a shade of red
I can't fully describe,
Between love and fear,
A place where hope resides.

And it captures my breath
With the beauty of its sway,
Its dignified stance
Not a stone's throw away.

Then, in my wonder,
A thought comes to mind,
What about the One
Who created such a sight?

And the clouds He fashioned
To be a calming grace,
A backdrop for the trees
Which we overlook in our haste.

How unjust we are,
To have His praise absent from our lips,

While we gaze
At the glorious creation of His.

Perfection unparalleled,
Beyond beauty and words,
Impossible except
By the Lord of the worlds.

Worthy of a million sighs,
And tears to fall in streams.
Subhanallahi wa bihamdihi,
Subhanallahil azeem.

Adil Iqbal (14)
HAFS Academy, Stratford

WORLD HUNGER

Have you been rich,
yet wanted more?
But have you ever,
thought of the poor.

Have you been hungry,
with the urge to eat?
Well, think about the poor,
'cause they have no more.

No shelter no heat,
no food no meat.
Life is a blessing for us,
so let's thank God by helping others.

There's no time to be selfish.
We can't let them perish.
So let's share our food,
changing everyone and their mood.

We have no gratitude,
we feel no remorse.
We force and demand,
whilst the poor sit there,
for an extra fund.

World Poetry Day,
a day to show and stand up

for our brothers and sisters in need.
So, let's make some noise,
and bring world hunger,
to an end together.

Rayhan Talukder (13)
HAFS Academy, Stratford

TREES

Trees are green.
We are so mean,
To those that keep us alive.

We hit, chop, and knock them down,
It happens here, there, all around.
Why can't we let them survive?

It is because of them, that we are here today,
To stand tall, and not decay.
It is so sad they can't always revive.

The pain of an axe, is too much,
Even from, the littlest touch.
For every death, we should plant five.

When we hit, we huff and heave,
After all this, what do we achieve
It's a tree's right that we deprive.

This is a message, for humankind,
It's so silly, how we have been so blind
We can save trees, if we all strive.

Thamim Islam (14)
HAFS Academy, Stratford

PARENTS

Raised me since day one,
Learnt how to talk at two.
Until seven, learnt how to tie my shoes,
Parents, they will never let you loose.

Put you through the real test of life,
Raised you all the way through.
Put you in a good school,
Now remember to be good back to them too.

Help them clean the house,
You should clean your own room.
Lessen the burden for them
And it will go back to you.

And never forget they will always love you,
They first created you
And now put you all the way through.
Still doing it now, so help them too,
And in the future, it will help you.

Huzaifa Mujahid Ali (13)
HAFS Academy, Stratford

PARENTS

No gift is greater,
You dried my tears when I was sad,
Why thank you Mum and Dad.
There is so much to add
And I'm sorry when I make you mad.

You nurtured me and took me with great care.
Every time I needed you,
You would always be there.

Parents, oh parents,
Forgive me for what I have done.
Parents would always give you adventure and fun.

Parents, oh parents
Your love is my main.
I will never give you a chance,
To stay mad and complain.

Having parents is such great fun,
Especially when you can have a laugh
Or play under the sun.

Hamid Alom (13)
HAFS Academy, Stratford

RAMADAN

Ramadan is undoubtedly blessed,
The month where you should not rest.
In this month, the Qur'an was delegated down,
It is more valuable than a crown.

The month where everyone was fasting,
I know the hours seem everlasting.
The month where everyone goes to pray,
Every single person will come to obey.

In this month, there is one rare night,
An extraordinary night full of light.
A charming Ramadan is here again,
So don't pause and sustain.

Enis Koesem (12)
HAFS Academy, Stratford

VOTES FOR WOMEN

Emily Davidson was a fighting suffragette.
She fought for the vote,
Yet nobody cared.

She tried her best to fight off the rest,
She walked on a racing track during the race.
Yet there was no lack of confidence upon her face.
She died that day
And still nobody cared.

After many more incidents and arrests,
In 1918, women were driven to succeed.
They had won the chase,
They had beaten the race,
At last, somebody cared.

Yet, we're still not finished,
We've only just gotten started,
The next generation.

Emma Moore (12)
Italia Conti Academy Of Theatre Arts, Islington

CROW

I envy you,
You majestic bird.
With no emotion, you understand
The simplest and most difficult of things.

With night-like feathers
You glide away from worries,
You gaze from the corners
And watch our emotions fly.

With passion, you soar,
Your war cries echo in our ears.
Ready to fight and, like a cat before its prey,
You pounce up to end it all.

They say you are a sign of death,
That you frighten people to their grave.
It is not true for we are alike,
Judged by our flaws, we have no control.

Ruby Da Cruz Heale (12)
Lady Margaret School, London

TEACHERS

Happy teacher,
Sad teacher,
Super self-obsessed teacher.
Hippy teacher,
Cool teacher,
Very over-dressed teacher.
Skinny teacher,
Fat teacher,
Nicely normal-sized teacher.
English teacher,
Maths teacher,
Super boring tech teacher.
Crazy teacher,
Bad teacher,
King of really good teacher.
Naughty teacher,
Fun teacher,
Mentally disturbed teacher.
Sassy teacher,
Mean teacher,
Do-what-you-want teacher.
Lazy teacher,
Art teacher,
Really loud sports teacher.
Selfie teacher,

Kind teacher,
Really annoying form teacher.
Clumsy teacher,
Strict teacher,
Way too cheerful headteacher.
And finally,
The normal teacher.

Maddy Kidd-May (12)
Lady Margaret School, London

NIGHT FALLS

The darkness of night falls,
The moon arises from its slumber.
The howling wolf calls,
As they completely outnumber.

A man steps forth,
Raising his mighty hand high.
Pointing towards the dark abyss,
Daring to claim what lies in the sky.

Scavenging for meat and prey,
Unleashing a terror in their way.
For the man stands against them,
Is claiming what lies in the sky.

Forward and backward,
They clash, they cry.
He rises up only to get battered
And lets out a tearful cry.

Maybe daring to claim what lies above,
May have been a mistake.
But that didn't stop the man,
Who was guided by fate.

Looked down upon by the wolves,
Kicking and shoving, looked like a fool.

For the man who stood against them,
Is miles away from claiming what lies in the sky.

Saber Kilwa
London Enterprise Academy, London

SAVE ME

Save me, from all this chaos floating,
Save me, from being a villain,
Save me, from losing my friend,
Save us, so it will never end.

Help me, I cannot breathe,
Help me, my fingers are turning into sticks,
Help me, I wanna see my dad,
Help us, so we'll never turn sad.

Talk to me, everything ain't gonna be the same,
Talk to me, I know you can't take me slave,
Talk to me, let them hear your name,
Talk to them, and say you won't cave.

Hear me, my lungs are pulling my heart in,
Hear me, it feels like they are churning it into sin,
Hear me, I don't know what to say but thank you,
Hear us, you're not alone.

My fingers are turning to stone,
Not only that it's now gone,
You can tell I'm not joking with this tone.
So please answer the phone.

Ashif Hussain
London Enterprise Academy, London

THE FASTIDIOUS FIRE

Scorching throughout the abyss,
Shining brighter than the ball of fire,
The flaming furnace of damnation
Stares at me with a grimace.

Crimson flames dance madly,
As people stare at it sadly.
Blazing hot sparks,
Making their marks.

From small smoke clouds,
Arising from ambiguity,
To a wild sensation,
This deadly thing burns throughout the nation.

Nothing will stand in its way,
If it does, it will burn and decay.
"It's a trap! Everyone must pray."

But there is hope, yes, hope.
That we will see the light of day,
That this dreadful fire will go away.
Hope for Grenfell and hope for all,
Because, together, nothing will make us fall.

Isa Abdussalam
London Enterprise Academy, London

THE FURIOUS FEAR OF TEARS

Tears,
What are they?
Weak.
Who wants to see them?
Nobody.
Why do they appear?
Fear.
How do you stop them?
You don't.
Who truly cares?
No one.

Why don't people ever see the importance of crying?
Or the true meaning behind one's tears?
Why is it that no powerful man cries
But every girl should?
Why is it that no one should be seen crying?
Yet, every doctor will tell you to release those harmful toxins
from your mind?
Why is it that, when a heart of glass breaks, the shards must
remain inside?
Every fragment cuts and kills.

Tears.
What are they?

Strength.
Who wants to see them?
You.
Why do they appear?
Courage.
How do you stop them?
Don't.
Who truly cares?
Everyone.

Sayeeda Islam (13)

Morpeth School, London

HATE SCORCHED THE FACE OF THE EARTH

The birth of evil,
The book of lies.

Tales of Heaven and Hell,
There was too much to tell.

Muffled cries
As darkness rose.

Those sly cat eyes,
Watching you as you died.

"Rise," a voice called.
"Rise from the ashes.

Cure those gashes
Made by knives.

Leave the dark,
Come into the light."
Only then will you see.

The birth of kindness,
The book of truth.

Birds chirped
As light rose.

Those peaceful cat eyes
Watching the sunrise.

Remember those steps you took,
How you overcame fear?

Now, help others
Tell the tales.

The tales of Heaven and Hell
But this time, it's your tale.

Your story,
Your life.

Shahara Ajmir (13)
Morpeth School, London

THE GAME OF LIFE

Life is like a board game,
Rolling the dice will change your life forever.
Whatever you want to be, will be your special aim.
Should you become a writer? A doctor? A banker?

If you move two spaces forward,
It might send you four spaces back.
You feel wonderful, you experience the good times,
Followed by the hard times and sadness that holds you
back.

Hoping to achieve in your lifetime,
Hoping not to lose,
Hoping to be the best we can,
Until the game ends.

Alisha Islam (12)
Morpeth School, London

THE SORROW OF THE DEVASTATED CROWN

The crown cries
When it is worn,
No one knows why.
It is devastated to be lonely.
The sorrow of the crown,
How I wonder.
It cries and cries,
Why, oh why?
I do not know why.
Let me talk to it,
See if it feels better.
No,
It does not,
Do not bother.

Amir Hamza (13)
Morpeth School, London

LIGHTNESS OF THE BUBBLE OF HATE

The bubble of hate is very light,
It's less than the weight of a feather.
It shows that hate will soon pass over,
It isn't going to stay with you forever.
It will soon go away like a fever.
Bubbles pop,
The hate will drop,
Love will rise,
Once and for all.

Fahmeda Azad (13)
Morpeth School, London

WHITE WOLF

Like a grey storm cloud,
A creeping silent shadow.
The wolf is like a thunderstorm,
He is powerful like the pouring rain,
He can be louder than a clap of thunder.

His dagger-like teeth and claws flash,
As it is caught in the moonlight.
His howling is like haunting music,
Beautiful but deadly.

His snow white coat is wrapped around his body,
Like a shiny coat of armour.
His tail like a frisky sword,
His ears like swivelling satellites,
Picking up the slightest of sounds.

His eyes like precious gold,
And he races with the wind,
His kins by his side.

Tasneem Mulla (13)
Plashet School, East Ham

POEMS ARE YOU

"You need to write a poem..."
Our minds switch off.
You hear the deep sighs from the class flooding you like a
tsunami rushing through the doors.
Some will ignore the whole sentence or only hear the word
'poem'.
Those who hear 'poem' will instantly write down all the
words that rhyme:
Cat, mat, hat...
I'm not saying rhyming is bad,
Rhyming is cool.
When I spell 'rhyme' wrong, it autocorrects to 'poem',
Rhyming sounds great but not on a piece of paper.
It's just words that just have the same sound
And if every sentence in a poem rhymed, it would be like a
Dr Seuss book.

There are many types of poems:
Haiku,
Pastoral
And many more.
Poems are a way to express yourself,
No matter the type.
Poems come straight from you,
There're no emojis and all that extra pizzazz disappears,
There's no one telling you how to feel,

What standards you must reach
And what rules you should comply with.
Society tells you what and how to feel,
But not poems.
Think of poems as a club,
Well done you just got accepted without even auditioning,
That's the concept of poems.

I've used the word 'poem' so many times,
But what is a poem?
I would be lying if I said I fully understood a definite meaning,
"Siri, what does this mean?"
Thinking the internet could solve all our worries and queries,
I wish it did.

Some stories are better untold,
So, some words are better undefined.
A poem could be anything,
Anything.
And when you say that there's always the one person who sniggers
And says something along the same format,
"So, even my baby brother knows what a poem is."
My definition of a poem is your life,
Your experiences,
Your background and much more.
I'm not the Oxford dictionary, but a poem could include anything

That makes you the person you are.

Poems are a way to channel your energy and emotions,
Like you're dumping all your emotions into a river.
Poems don't always have to be this or that,
Your poem can be 'normal',
Whatever 'normal' is.

The biggest worries for teenagers is our insecurities,
But guess what, insecurities are a gateway to self-love.
Call it vanity or egotism or whatever you want,
Or even search Tumblr quotes to describe whatever it is.
I can tell you what is so much better
Than Pinterest and Tumblr:
You.
You are writing about anything you're passionate about,
Or even what happened at school,
But it came from you and your magical brain

While writing this I have just developed a theory.
A poem is you.

Muna Elmi (14)
Plashet School, East Ham

RAMADAN

The month we love the best
Is truly blessed,
This is the month
When the Qur'an was sent.
This is the month
Where we increase our iman
This is the month of Ramadan.

This is the month
Where we fast and pray
Throughout the day,
But not to play 'cause
This is the month of Ramadan.

This is the month
Where we remove our greed
To get good deed,
By paying zakah
To people in need.

At the end of the day
We break our chain,
With a bite of kajoor
And with a sip of water
And start a new fast at dawn.

Alaina Siddiqui (12)
Plashet School, East Ham

DEAR MOTHER

If I could give you diamonds,
For each tear you cry for me,
If I could give you sapphires,
For every second you suffer for me.
If I could give you gold,
For each truth you have helped me see,
If I could give you rubies,
For each moment I tear your heart.

Then you'll be a precious treasure that shines
As bright as the sun.
That would match
The sparkles in your kind and loving eyes.

Your smile can light a thousand hearts,
Your gracious never-ending love
Can wash away all fears.
There are no words that can come close
To define who you are.

And, if at times,
I may seem ungrateful,
I was to say that I truly hope you see,
That nothing you have done for me has been forgotten
And day by day,
You just mean more to me.

So remember Mother,
Whatever you do and whatever you say,
You will always be my
Beloved mother
At the end of the day.

Norin Khatun (13)
Plashet School, East Ham

ONE LAST BREATH

Her heart beating,
Meeting her end,
Leaving her to fend,
For all those times,
When we used to play
And look at the day
On the sea bay.
How you left,
Making me heft your hole.
How I felt,
As you knelt for above,
What you meant to me?
A part of me flew away
Like an incompetent bee,
Astray from me.
Whirling, churning,
My heart burning,
Embracing her hand,
Leaving for God's land,
Memories, treasuries,
I fell in misery,

Her one last breath.

Ashwina Kalanathan (14)
Plashet School, East Ham

HOPE...

It is a fragile butterfly
In a vulture's world,
It is a glimmer of light
In the eternal darkness.
It is the emerging truth
In the midst of lies,
It is a spot of peace
In the universe of war.
It is the bloom of red
In the emerald-green,
It is the bittersweet chocolate
In times of depression.
It is hope that mends
The shattered soul.

Nazifa Islam (14)
Plashet School, East Ham

ACHING DESIRE

My brain,
A prisoner.
My heart,
So naive.

The monsters,
Once under my bed,
Now in my head.
Gnawing
And conquering.

My thoughts
Turning silent,
Violent,
Deafening.

Look through my eyes,
A broken soul
In disguise.

Look through my lies.
Can't you see?
I'm breaking inside.

Humaira Khondkar (14)
Plashet School, East Ham

LIFE

Life can bring you joy,
Life can bring you sadness,
Life can bring you hate,
Life can bring you madness.
But, it's just those little things,
Life isn't so bad for you or for me.
Love and hope,
Emotions that we're feeling,
So think about life being worth living.

Alessio Capozzi
Rickmansworth School, Rickmansworth

ART

A broken chain,
yet I still stand there.
No anchor,
yet the boat
still floats,
bobbing up and down,
resting on the one place
as the current pushes,
pulls,
trying to set it to a path.
The cage door is open
welcoming and inviting
yet hostile and so very demeaning
and, though there is no glass,
I crash into it,
like a bird on a clear day

the doors that lead to heaven,
they close at my sight
the wrecked gate to hell
it clears me off instantly.
The pathway to earth,
into life,
is hazy to me
with my 20/20 vision.
And on this chair,

my seed was planted
and in this room,
I started sprouting.
In this place,
my flower blossomed
in the cold darkness.
There was no one to watch
my fierce and hungry movement
my greed
that fed me
my salvation-my hate
so clear the despise.
Yet so crystal the love
my heart weighs me down
as my mind moves on
and still,
I am.
Not a single breath
drawn from within me
inhaled from the out
my lungs were ripped
the haggard breaths already stolen
my fingers point towards the victim
as my hands grab the perpetrator
and the statue I am
is entitled to this mess
the mess they want

to distract the others
the mess they call art.

Mahrou Marjan Meem (13)
St Saviour's And St Olave's School, Southwark

MY LOOKS DON'T DEFINE WHO I AM

How would you describe me?
Pretty? Ugly? Short with long hair?
Those things however are just the things you see.
But, based on these things, you shouldn't really care.

You see, what you see with your eyes
Are absolute lies,
Because, what your eyes do is deceive,
Which leads to the things you perceive.

But these things are all fake,
Because they are based on the perceptions you make.
You see, you don't judge by colour, skin or race,
I mean, you don't even judge people by their face.

I don't care about your looks externally,
I care about your looks internally.
Sorry, did I offend you? Don't feel bad,
I'm just talking about the things that make me mad.

Tall, short, skinny, fat,
Don't judge by those things, don't be a cat.
We were all created in God's image,
So why carry so much baggage
About the way we look?

Deborah Esan (15)
St Saviour's And St Olave's School, Southwark

AN EFFECT

The area around me is chilling,
I see a figure collapsed before me.
Quivering, I attempt to comfort them
"No!"
Confused, I fall to the rich and fruitful dirt.
It is clear now, I am but a simple spectator,
The world around me is only a fraud,
Plucked from somebody's cavern of creativity.
The characters forced to relive the same bitter, depressing
life over and over,
Like a broken record repeating the same sad tune.
But, what use is this world if it is only a figment of one's
imagination?

Perhaps to escape your own reality?
Or change your perception?
The character stands, sniffling
And gazes directly through me.
Vision is cracking,
World is blackening,
A speeding cacophony bursts by my ears,
My mind's eye is closing.
I open my eyes
And begin to read again.
Oh, how I despise being distracted.

Elle Simmonds (12)
St Saviour's And St Olave's School, Southwark

YOU HAVE TO LOVE BOOKS

You have to love books,
They can build your knowledge so much.
Read them in the morning, evening
And even whilst you're having lunch.

You have to love books,
Tattered and antique or new.
Just remember to try new books,
Anyone could be flawless for you.

You have to love books,
Just think of the wonderlands they can take you to.
From magical worlds to the darkest of places,
It's amazing just what they can do.

You have to love books,
Any type of book!
Surreal books, factual books,
Imaginative and interactive books,
Take one look and they'll have you hooked.

So why are you still here reading this,
Come on, get out of here, shoo!
Go find yourself a book to read,
The book that is perfect for you!

Grace Webb (12)
St Saviour's And St Olave's School, Southwark

POACHING FOR BEARS

G reedy, the petrified polar bear stalks around for food,
L ike an ant, unaware that the merciless poacher is in a hopeful mood.
O blivious, several moments is all that it takes,
B eaten, the clueless polar bear doesn't know what difference it makes,
A s it feels like a shocking thump,
L ike a ragged doll, the force of the bullet makes it slump.

W eakly, the blood of the dead drips down,
A s slowly as a snail, the staining red liquid seeps onto the ground,
R acing, the blood runs across the ice,
M ixing, the pool of red has the poacher mesmerised.
I t once stalked around for food,
N ow, lying down in a hopeless mood,
G rounded, the bear is defeated and the poachers have suceeded.

Hannah Lin (12)
St Saviour's And St Olave's School, Southwark

YOU ARE YOU

To revise and to learn can help you in this world,
To read can take you to places you've never seen before.
To be resilient can conquer all your troubles in this world,
To respect and be respected for who you really are,
To never change and stand tall and fly like a crane.

When your soul is about to cry and your eyes can't stay dry,
Keep calm and cool and don't cry up a pool.
Be strong and proud like you're the queen of the crowd,
Do not let emotions lead the way.
You are you,
Let it stay that way.

Be a leader, not a follower,
Be proud, be a warrior,
Because you live for a purpose.
Think like a curtain:
Shade all the darkness,
But let the light shine through,
Because you are you.

Nasrin Kasim (12)
St Saviour's And St Olave's School, Southwark

LIAR'S MOON

My heart tells lies
Under the fake light of the moon.

It promises to bring me comfort,
But disappears by morning.
As I sit in the darkness,
I wait for the moon.
Sometimes it's there as a half,
Sometimes, only a fraction,
Like a wicked grin, alluring me.
It looks down on me,
Whereas I can only watch from below,
Watch as it leaves.

When he is whole, I can see
The tiny fraction of our planet,
I find myself.
I know that I can't stand the liar's moon,
The moon is nothing but a rock
Up in the sky,
Only reflecting light.
The liar's moon.
Standing on its own,
Never feeling lonely,
Its pearly whiteness,

A speck of dust.
The liar's moon.

Romesa Kashif (13)
St Saviour's And St Olave's School, Southwark

POACHED BY POLLUTION

The Earth was once covered in life,
But now, most are stabbed with a knife.

Our green land, now a landfill,
Eaten by them, they soon lay still.

Their population is rapidly decreasing,
As sea levels rise and ice is melting.

Death, what a powerful word,
Right now, it is happening to the world.

It's our fault they are dying,
It's our fault that we are dying.

Soon, Earth will be lifeless,
As we didn't show it kindness.

We take everything for granted,
But later, it is all regretted.

Animals are dying around us,
We are destroying Earth,
We are destroying us.

We cause pollution,
We cause death,
Was the world meant to meet its end?

Raima Kashif (11)
St Saviour's And St Olave's School, Southwark

THE CAUSE OF THE WORLD'S DEMISE

As the world increases in numbers,
Overpopulation is truly here.
It is something to truly fear,
If we don't act now, the world's demise will soon be here.

The world is a cup,
And everyone in the world is the water being poured into it.
And now, because of overpopulation,
The cup will soon overflow.

Now, if we don't do something,
The world will be covered with people.
Food will disappear,
And the human race may never reappear.
If we don't act now, we soon won't be here.

Overpopulation is the true threat here,
It is something we must fear.
It is what causes more problems here,
And the world's demise will soon be near.

Mary Konadu (13)
St Saviour's And St Olave's School, Southwark

GLOBAL WARMING

Polar bears are disappearing
And extinction they are nearing,
Global warming melts their ice,
For polar bears, that isn't nice.
The arctic's getting really hot,
Will global warming stop, or not?

Baby seals are being drowned,
The solution still hasn't been found.
The way to stop this global warming,
Taking poor animals' lives without warning.
Thousands of animals dead, oh wow,
We have to stop this now, but how?

Into the sea, debris floats away,
Not to take another life I pray.
Why do we do this? Why, oh why?
Just talking about it brings tears to the eye.
I watched the news in disbelief,
The waste has destroyed the coral reef.

Teniola Oduala (12)
St Saviour's And St Olave's School, Southwark

A STORM

A storm is rolling in,
Quick and quiet.
But we are ignoring
That this storm will bring death.
Striking the innocent with stealth.
This storm will bring rain,
Flood, heat and hurricane.
This storm will bring change to the air we breathe
And the things we've made.
This storm will bring divide,
Causing conflict, hostility
And we will collide.
This storm is unstoppable, helpless, unchanging,
This storm is stirring, awakening and raging.
"Where did it come from?" I hear you ask,
The selfishness of humans, now we have a task:
To care for our world, it's the first and our last.
A storm is rolling in, quick and quiet.

Akonte Tyger (12)
St Saviour's And St Olave's School, Southwark

CRACK

Crack! Ice is floating away,
The baby seal slips under the waves,
No one is there to save the day.

Spill! A container of oil stains a coat,
From fluffy milky white
To a black as murky as a disintegrating boat.

'Clean the oceans, save the ice!'
Go the seal's plea to save what's nice.

Ouch! Is it just me, or is the Earth getting warmer?
Fatal fumes choke our once azure skies,
A planet-sized oven or maybe a sultry sauna.

Us humans need to band together,
Let's help the seals
And let our ice last much, much longer.

Tabitha O'Callaghan (12)
St Saviour's And St Olave's School, Southwark

INSIDE MY HEAD

Inside my head,
If you'd heard what I said,
Maybe all this emotion could set things in motion,
For the better
Or the worse.

Inside my head,
If you'd heard what I said,
Maybe the quiet girl's silence would unfurl.
Words would unravel,
Whatever they were.

Inside my head,
If you'd heard what I said,
Maybe my shell would be cracked,
My reputation sacked.
Read me like a book,
Come take a look.

The stories,
The rhymes,
The music,
The signs.

The smiles,
The frowns,

The ups
And the downs.

Elsie McDowell (13)
St Saviour's And St Olave's School, Southwark

OVER-STUDDED

Imagine a lady with several diamonds in her ear,
Imagine them proliferating without fear.
Imagine there is nowhere else to put the diamonds,
Imagine that.

Imagine how many people are in this world,
Imagine how and why we mulitply.
Imagine soon there will be nowhere for them to live and die,
Imagine that.

Imagine those people and that lady with nowhere to go in
these situations,
Imagine them like a kettle.
Imagine yourself filling it to the brim, then it's full,
Imagine that.

Imagine these people as if they were our planet,
Over-studded.

Temi Odukale (12)
St Saviour's And St Olave's School, Southwark

WHAT HAVE WE DONE?

What have we done?
Litter is on the ground,
Polar bears will drown,
A nightmare come true.

I do not like to brag,
But this world has become mad.
As acid rain chokes the trees,
Destroyed; I know.

We probably didn't know,
We are in a daze,
While we drown in pollution's haze,
We are not able to breathe,
Because our trees are not at ease.

What have we done?
Our clear water's gone,
Natural resources are done,
Global warming has come.

Lilyana Baird-Thomas (11)
St Saviour's And St Olave's School, Southwark

MOTHER NATURE'S LAW: I AM DYING INSIDE

I am the Earth, the mother of them all,
But I am dying inside.
Each day, a piece of me burns.
I just want to lie down and rest,
But my body will burn, bit by bit.
These cruel people of the world,
They want to see me suffer,
They want to choke me.
Your chemicals poison me.
After everything I've done,
This is how you repay me?
What did I do to deserve
This kind of treatment?
Have you thought of how life will carry on?
I am warning you, stop this madness, or else.

Tosin Agoro (12)
St Saviour's And St Olave's School, Southwark

OUR GENERATION

Who am I to have my neck burning,
Electronics taking over our lives,
A noise-box desperate to be turning.

This little box, our money, our entertainment,
Our shopping order,
Parks, zoos and family forgotten
As they get shorter.

Sometimes I worry what life will be like for my daughter,
This electronic farmer fattening her up for slaughter.
Only playing games and taking naps,
Soon the world will be swimming in apps.

Playing football and playgrounds are becoming outdated,
If only Steve Jobs knew what he'd created.
Technology is on the loose, there's no going back,
Now the whole world is in an electronic shack.

If only grandparents were still in this era,
They'd open our eyes and make things clearer.

We have a shortage of people who are still on a mission,
To try and get Apple and Samsung to listen.

If only we could start this new creation,
But the world's been addicted to this electronic generation.

Finn Parker (13)
St Thomas More High School For Boys, Westcliff-On-Sea

WHEN A BIRD DROPS ITS MINE

This was the second time
That the sirens blared,
This time, the people knew
And the people were scared.

Last time, shells rained from the sky,
Whistling on their way down,
As if happy, innocent people wouldn't die.

But now was part two,
No time to lock doors,
Mum, Dad and child,
Here comes 'the war to end all wars'.

A roar from the sky
Makes heads turn up high,
Mothers tell their children not to cry,
They say everything will be alright,
But, of course, they lie.

People don't know what is yet to come,
For they have never experienced
This type of bomb.

The first lands on a house,
The city looks in awe,

Because they have never seen something like this before.

Orange, yellow and red,
The inferno has spread,
Buildings ready to collapse,
"Get to the bunker!" a warden said.

At age sixty-four,
I remember what happened before:
Gunfire and bombs
England was torn.

A siren blares me back to 1939
When I hear a bomb drop,
The bird has dropped his mine.

It's falling, falling,
Falling from the abyss
Above my head, it's falling
There will be no near miss.

It happened so slow,
I heard the whistling grow closer
It opened four feet from my toe
I saw the inferno grow
The fire glow
I accepted what I had to know
Was I alive?
No.

Charlie Betts (14)
St Thomas More High School For Boys, Westcliff-On-Sea

I LOVE NOTHING MORE THAN MY PS4

There's one thing adults don't understand,
Headphones on, a tube of Pringles in hand,
A comfy sofa and a super-sized screen
Is all a lad needs to have fun with his team.

I'm Harry Kane, about to place it in the goal,
Fire already, I'm really on a roll.

Up behind comes Pique, sliding in to challenge,
But he really looks pale,
He nearly got me, but he just isn't great.
I am amazingly powerful and winning this race.

This team doesn't know I'm a pro at Fifa,
I should really be playing Wembley Arena.

I'm in the zone, having fun on Fortnite,
Tooled up and kitted, ready for a fight.

My mate pulled out a blue AR,
But the opposition had a golden SCAR.
One shot, two shot, three and he's down,
Now to jump in and save him, so we could win the crown.

Now I am on the front line in Call of Duty WWII,
Playing Team Deathmatch and we're starting to lose.

Had to get my game up to save the team,
It's dark, it's bloody and often extreme.

As a soldier, I have my team's backs,
Me and my troops fight off all attacks.

Grand Theft Auto, I'm still finding my way,
Gangsters, cars, guns, what else can I say?

I'm not top of the game, but it's fun to play,
Adults don't understand, but still want their say.

Paddy-Joe Brandon-Blatch (14)
St Thomas More High School For Boys, Westcliff-On-Sea

DEALING WITH LIFE AND EMOTIONS

Life has a lot of strife,
Temptations that make you thrive.
Issues that cause wet tissues
And tricks that put you on the wrong track.

Anger is an emotion,
An emotion that builds up with you.
Then creates a bad motion,
Causing a lot of commotion.

Sadness is the opposite of anger,
Making you depressed,
Until you feel compressed.
Hide against a wall, curl yourself into a ball.
Sadness will follow you wherever you go.

Happiness is a source of delight,
Making you feel good all around.
Look at me jump, clearing the dump,
Spreading the love, building like a dove.

Love is a search,
Looking all over Earth.
Searching far and wide,
Setting the bar high.

Life eventually ends,
Becoming old and gaining age.
Pale, bald heads and everlasting range,
Don't look in the past, look in the future.

Death is not the best,
Heaven or Hell,
Right or wrong,
A string of decisions always prolonged.

The afterlife is a crazy life,
Heaven is good,
Hell is rude,
Where you end up, time only knows.

Anthony Otuorimuo (13)
St Thomas More High School For Boys, Westcliff-On-Sea

RACE DAY

Up at the crack of dawn,
Training hard for the competition.
My mind starting to take over,
But my body still keeps going.

Alarm set early,
Race day now beckons.
Kitbag set and ready,
Tomorrow I will go off fast but make sure I'm steady.

Time for race day,
Only a few hours to go.
One train ride
And the course awaits.

Rain is now falling with no mercy,
This course is treacherous, muddy and hilly.
The race is now ten minutes away
And my competitors surround me.

Bang! The race is off,
Thousands sprint up the hill.
Like a pack of wolves,
All battling for number one.

Beads of sweat drip down my face,
As we approach halfway.

Slowly catching the front of the pack,
But they seem so far away.

Now we approach, the final straight,
My body is aching, but I know the end is close.
A final push to the finish line
And then finally, it will be done.

It's all over,
Legs caked in mud.
Spit flung across my face,
But that's why I love cross country.

Luke Randall (13)
St Thomas More High School For Boys, Westcliff-On-Sea

FRIEND

Hello.

First, I learned your name
Not knowing that, soon,
You would bring me down to shame.
Letting you into my deepest secrets,
I thought I could trust you,
But now I start to feel it.

Then.

You told me to change my ways,
Because I always had your back, I did it anyway.
Gel, knots, everything in my hair,
I always did it for you.
Even though it brought me pain that I couldn't bear.

Now.

All my secrets have gone viral,
Now my life is a never-ending spiral.
My heart has a big puncture,
Life is a sinking ship, with no function.

In the beginning, I was in control of my life,
But now, on my chest lies a kitchen knife.

All the memories of our 'good times',
Me changing myself a couple hundred times.

I always covered up all my scars,
All of this, only just to be called a 'try-hard'.

I'm even losing control of my knife,
I give it to you,
So you can end my life.

Now, I always had your back,
But did you, friend?

Heshan Mahendra (13)
St Thomas More High School For Boys, Westcliff-On-Sea

CHOICES

We are all brothers,
Yet we choose to fight amongst one another.
We choose our colours, red or blue,
But that doesn't have to be me or you.
We choose to unite,
We choose the wrong fight.
We should be arms in arms,
Yet we choose to kill with arms.
We are oppressed,
Yet still obsessed
With killing one another.
A brother kills a brother.

Taking lives,
Killing with knives,
A simple tool turned weapon,
Could killing be an obsession?
The knives used to cut rope,
Now used to cut a strand of hope.
To end someone's life,
To cause so much strife.
Do you want this blood on your hands?
Do you understand?
An innocent knife,
Can end a life.

The pain that's caused is catastrophic,
In their eyes, you may turn out satanic.
Your choice and destiny is your decision,
That's why it's your personal mission
To exclaim and to make a happy voice.
To make the real choices.
We need to realise that we choose fate,
Realise before it's too late.

Lemuel Munyaradzi Bultman (13)

St Thomas More High School For Boys, Westcliff-On-Sea

GHAST

Floating around,
In buildings, in cars,
They cannot be seen,
But they will give you scars.

Sometimes you may hear them,
In the echoes of the night,
But you will not see them,
Even with willpower and might.

How they came to be,
No one knows,
But most of all,
They will always impose.

Rumour has it,
That they never die,
But even if that's true,
They will always lie.

The truth about these magical creatures,
Isn't the fact that they cannot be seen,
It's that they might meet you,
When you're not too keen.

You shouldn't ask me,
How they appear,

But they have no apathy,
And are so clear.

"Why are they so ghastly?"
I hear you ask,
Do not fret, my friend,
It's merely a Gastly.

Appearing from the bushes,
Dead on the floor,
Becoming soulless and lifeless,
They do abhor.

Truly mysterious,
Very mischievous,
Not to be encountered,
Do not ask me what if.

Oliver Stanton (14)
St Thomas More High School For Boys, Westcliff-On-Sea

WAR

Men leave their homes
As air raid sirens begin to sound,
Evacuees escaping cities
And bombs start to be dropped.

Whisked away without a say,
"Why can't I stay another day?"
Young boys decide to be brave,
As mothers wave their daughters away.

Trenches become a sanctuary,
As many lie dead back in the bay.
Seas become divine red wine,
While soldiers begin to cry.

Trench foot spreading,
German troops advancing.
Old men are laughing,
As their vision starts fading.

Machine guns popping,
Men are dropping.
Humanity failing,
Children are wailing.

Peace at last,
We cry "Hurrah!"

Hugs and kisses all around,
As ashes fall to the ground.

War is over,
Or just for a moment
As war will come again,
When will the bombardment end?

War is death,
War is hate,
War is freedom,
War is a friend.

War is here,
War is there,
War is everywhere,
War will never end.

Henry Tilley (13)
St Thomas More High School For Boys, Westcliff-On-Sea

DEATH, PAIN, SUFFERING

Whistling, whistling in the air,
Bodies, bodies everywhere,
Blood, blood everywhere,
Death, death everywhere.

The smell of blood fills the air,
German bullets miss my head.
Bayonets are in my friends,
Suddenly, "Artillery, take cover!"

A ring in my ears,
A blur in my eyes,
A wound in my left leg,
And a gun at my side.

A whistle in my head,
"Push onwards men!"
Pulled to my feet by my commander.
I try turning, but am stopped by barbed wire.

The heat, the flaming-hot heat,
I hear men shout, "It burns! It burns!"
I look over my shoulder and see a man
With the face of an elephant.

His weapon spits the breath of a dragon,
Clearing out trenches
And roasting the men alive.
Death, pain, suffering, all stuck in my head.

I draw my rifle and aim for his head,
The burst of the rifle throws me back.
I know I hit my target,
Because the death, pain and suffering have all stopped.

Aaran Wingrove-Smith (13)
St Thomas More High School For Boys, Westcliff-On-Sea

MOTHER NATURE

She can be vicious, taking life away,
She flicks the switch between light and day.
Seven billion inhabitants, to her all mere,
Her unreadable actions can leave us in fear.

Freezing conditions or boiling hot,
Constantly under her shadow, bowing at her feet.
Her seas split nations and races apart,
She never changed, not from the start.

A flooded town or droughted green land,
To vegetation-ridden forest and beaches covered in sand.
She was the creator and will always be,
She made the animals in the land, sky and sea.

But we all see her beauty, stunning and amazing,
Then after, fires and tornadoes blazing.
She leaves a country torn with no signs of life
And leaves behind ruins, no chance of saving.

But why's she angry, powerful and rough?
There's always a reason, but this time it's us,
We destroy her creations by leaving litter,
Do you now understand why she's so bitter?

Leo Palmer (14)
St Thomas More High School For Boys, Westcliff-On-Sea

DISGUISED

Souls,
They are the sacred relics of the body,
Dark and unnoticed like a shadow,
Where our lives are kept in rhythm, much like a melody,
Calm and peaceful, like an ocean they flow.

Determine our long awaited fate and destiny,
Tranquilised and motionless is how they act,
But don't get complacent, they are far more powerful than
any weaponry,
Ultimately, a lot more precious than an ancient artefact.

Sophistication is an understatement,
Incredibly hidden in one of our body's chambers,
Holds much more value than any payment,
At the same time, they can lead to various dangers.

One of the many gifts we can't study,
Impossible that it's man-made, it is perfectly devised,
They have a long chain of secrets, some are bloody,
It's a shame we can't unlock their full meaning as they are
disguised.

Stefan Protic (14)
St Thomas More High School For Boys, Westcliff-On-Sea

MENTALITY

We all spend nine months in a womb,
Yet some live a few years, then they're in a tomb.
So many misguided youths,
Blinded by a warped and twisted truth.

So many wasted young,
All been killed with a knife.
It's so scary that people out there,
Can take a human life.

They all put up a facade
To make themselves feel tough,
When truth be told,
It's all been a little rough.

They've lost so many friends,
The killings never end,
It's just a vicious cycle,
Either you kill or you're dead.

And, technically, it's not the knife that does the deed,
It's something they do unconsciously.
They send out a message subliminally,
They're all diagnosed with some malady,
All of them sufferers of that gang mentality.

Omotade Adekunle Atobatele (13)
St Thomas More High School For Boys, Westcliff-On-Sea

THE NIGHT

The day ends and fear sets in,
Not because of the night.
Tonight, again, I will not win,
Because of what's within.

Some have fears of animals, which scratch and bite and
roar,
Others have fears of people, people thirsty for their blood.
And some only fear things that they do not know for sure,
I, however, do not fear rational things like earthquakes,
storms or floods.

My greatest fear is what comes in the night,
You may think it's stupid when I tell you what it is.
You may think that I have no reason for my fright,
You could even say that it is ignorance.

But you have not felt the pain,
Of being alone again and again.

Alone with only thoughts I've had,
A lot of them sadden me.
And others make me just feel bad,
Only some are happy.

George Sandell (12)
St Thomas More High School For Boys, Westcliff-On-Sea

TEACHERS

Teachers can sometimes be the worst things around,
Teachers can turn your frowns upside down.
Teachers are the smartest thing around,
Teachers will teach you, even if their hearts are up.

Teachers are the reason why we have our jobs,
Teachers are the reason why we have costs.
But how much can it cost for people to listen?
Don't blame anyone for your bad grades because you
should've listened.

Distractions are the locked doors of the hallway,
Teachers are the keys to succeed.
But the doors can only be opened if you trust me,
Because teachers are and will be the best around.

Now that is all I have to say,
I hope you all have fun writing your essays,
Remember what I have written today
And remember to never leave a blank page to rot away.

Sean David (13)
St Thomas More High School For Boys, Westcliff-On-Sea

THE START OF A MAGICAL JOURNEY

There once was a boy named Harry,
Destined to be a star,
His parents were killed by Voldemort,
Who gave him a lightning scar.

A silver-haired man named Dumbledore,
Left him on Privet Drive.
When his aunt found him outside her door,
She knew it was the end of her life.

When he was taken to the zoo,
He somehow talked to a snake.
But when his cousin shoved him down the loo,
His smile quickly turned fake.

Soon he arrived at Hogwarts,
The very best wizarding school.
When he looked at his lessons, oh there were lots,
He suddenly thought learning was cool.

He became friends with Ron and Hermione
And they formed a wizarding clan.
They agreed to embark on a quest with him
And so their adventures began.

Areeb Khan (12)
St Thomas More High School For Boys, Westcliff-On-Sea

THE CUP

The first half was boring,
No team was scoring,
I could see my brother snoring
As I walked into the changing room.

Now we're one-nil down,
Our smiles turn into frowns.
My manager shouted,
"You're playing like clowns!"
Quick, free kick,
Striker did a flick
Around the defender,
The shot was a bender.

The ball flew in
To the top bins.
My manager shouted,
"Now we can win!"
Now it's one-all,
While we fought for the ball.
Their defence's brick wall
Was stopping it all.

With a minute left,
"A corner!" said the ref,
The ball swung in,
We knew we'd win.

Two-one up,
We lifted the cup.
The team left it late,
But boy, it felt great.

Freddie Treacher (14)
St Thomas More High School For Boys, Westcliff-On-Sea

ON THE PITCH WE'RE ALL THE SAME

On the pitch, we're all the same,
On the pitch, history's made,
On the pitch, you see me through a distant shot.

In the crowd, we're all the same,
In the crowd, we all feel emotion,
In the crowd, we all want to win,
Never want to lose, settle for a draw.

On the pitch, we're all the same,
Panting, running,
Shooting, missing,
Not knowing the dreaded thing that will come.

In the crowd, while we wait, we're all the same,
We wait with bated breath,
We wait with tension,
We wait with exhileration.

On the pitch, we're all the same,
Nervous to take our shot,
You freeze,
Run, shoot, score.

In the crowd and on the pitch,
There's tears of sadness,
There's tears of joy.

Zachary Sossou (14)
St Thomas More High School For Boys, Westcliff-On-Sea

OVER THE EDGE

The shells come down,
What are we doing here?
Looking for cover, we run.

We jump over the edge, into war,
What are we doing here?
Running for our lives.

We run, we take cover,
What are we doing here?
We dive, we hope.

We shoot at the enemy lines,
What are we doing here?
Again, looking for cover.

We aim, we shoot,
What are we doing here?
We kill, we survive.

We won't die.
What are we doing here?
We will forever live.

We won't die,
What are we doing here?
We will live in the hearts of future generations.

We saved your world,
What are we doing here?
We won, we have always won.

We may be dead now,
Why not come and see us?
We won for you.

Luca Apicella (13)
St Thomas More High School For Boys, Westcliff-On-Sea

THE WORLD CUP

The universal event occurs once every four years,
Upholding national pride, support, shout and cheer.
Each country goes to succeed their opportunity,
With all the fans forming an international community.

Fans and players unite to hear the anthem,
The lyrics on screen, they stand and shout them.
Iconic players funnel out onto the pitch,
Walking past the trophy, unaffordable even for the rich.

The referee puts his whistle to his mouth and blows,
Amongst the crowd, flags and banners flow.
The game's kicked off, the ball's in play,
Two opposing sides, it could go either way.

Thirty-two countries,
At least one special to you.
There can only be one winner
Which one will you choose?

Luca Butteriss (14)
St Thomas More High School For Boys, Westcliff-On-Sea

WAR REALITY

When the battalion dies,
There will be shrieks and cries.
However, the truth will be shrouded with lies.

Every shot results in a casualty
And explosions in the distance echo loudly,
While the enemy keeps shooting, grinning proudly.

Their objective is a mistake,
Which will take major out-takes
In the young lives of the future.

When the deed was done, there was silence,
The guns finished blazing,
They can now acknowledge their violence.

They take swift glances,
Their vision enhances
And they accept that they took their chances.

However, this is just a small part,
As the war rages on and on,
When will the next battle start?

Will Hood (14)
St Thomas More High School For Boys, Westcliff-On-Sea

WHAT ARE WE DOING?

There are 100 of us in the air,
What are we doing?
We are taking hits,
We are going down.

Jump? Why? Hope is evaporating,
What are we doing?
We are frightened,
We are scared.

Where will we go?
What are we doing?
We are going to die,
We are hopeless.

All the eye can see is blue,
What are we doing?
Will I ever see my family?
Who will save us?

So many questions,
What are we doing?
We are all screaming,
We have all given up.

We are all strangers,
What are we doing?
We are distant,
We are in the hands of the enemy.

Will I ever see the light again?
What are we doing?
Seriously,
What are we doing?

William Seymour (12)
St Thomas More High School For Boys, Westcliff-On-Sea

TIME'S UP

The whistle goes,
Adrenaline starting to flow,
The thoughts of where this could go!

Arms are shaking like never before,
Legs can't bear the sheer force.
The feeling that you want to divorce,
With everything you've ever seen.

You let go,
Departed from everything you know
And submerge into the unknown.
Break for breath, but it's not enough.

Your heart is pounding,
Gasping for breath,
But all you receive is an intense test
Of power, stamina, knowledge and rest.

You rest,
Laying on the deep sea bed
And you gaze at the boats above your head.
You see the board from where you jumped,
Into your unknown death.

Alfie Williams (14)
St Thomas More High School For Boys, Westcliff-On-Sea

ENDLESS WAR

Whether we're the knights in the sky,
The ghosts in a desert or the rats in the mud,
We are people's children, waiting for our turn to go.

Watching over the top, ready for the enemies to come,
Waiting to kill another's child
And to see them fall in a lost brother's blood.

The screams of men ringing through our heads.
We're scared and frightened,
Wondering what our fate will be.
Telling stories of days before the war,
Just out of reach and unreal.
Not even the thought of going to war,
Family and home isn't real anymore.

I almost feel bad for them,
As they are going through the same as us
In this endless war.

Olly Robinson (13)
St Thomas More High School For Boys, Westcliff-On-Sea

ME VS THE WORLD

Are you ready to take a life again?
To kill? It's too cold, but it's clear.
I will kill if it's time,
I will kill for my flag,
I will kill to protect,
Take a life to spare a life.

Why would you go down that road again?
Everything is the same.
The same evil dictator,
The same war,
The same men,
Dying and dying all over again.
No one cares.
Government uses soliders as a pawn,
In this massive, chaotic game of chess.

It doesn't even matter anymore.
Why is life worth living?
Why are we fighting?
Why are some richer?
Don't act like God,
Don't take a life,
We are all the same.

Milan Jomon (14)
St Thomas More High School For Boys, Westcliff-On-Sea

I AM WHAT I AM

I am what I am,
I am my books, stories, myths,
I am my strength, sense, scene.
I know what I am.

I am what I am,
I am my fun, friendship, freedom,
I am my blank canvas, my imagination, my creativity.
I know what I am.

I am what I am,
I am my past, present, future,
I am my work, my play, my rest.
I know what I am.

I am what I am,
I am my friends, family, religion,
I am my fear, darkness, my rage.
I know what I am.

You are what you are,
You are your personality, family and friends,
You are your hopes, ambitions, dreams.
You know what you are.

George Standley (12)
St Thomas More High School For Boys, Westcliff-On-Sea

A FRIEND

Life is a mountain,
Without a team, the incline is so steep.
To climb to the peak,
Is a dream impossible to reach.

Life will lie,
It will supress the light
And only show false truths,
Just in spite.

Life will utter harsh whispers in your ear,
It will distill fear,
Just to leer.

A friend can abate the activity,
A friend can dispell the deceit,
A friend can provide clarity in the haze,
A friend can lull the pain.

Life is a burden,
It could cripple the strongest person alive.
My best advice,
Is to find a friend who will support you in life.

Harvey Hysop (13)
St Thomas More High School For Boys, Westcliff-On-Sea

THE OPEN SEA

The work that makes me sigh,
Parting, quickly escaping
As a spark lights in my eye,
Freedom is awaiting.

Launching with all my might,
Rough, sleepy waves crashing at my hull.
Breaking free into the blinding sunlight,
What were severe waves, now go lull.

My heartbeat slows to the rhythm of the waves,
I feel no boundries in this sacred place.
This life, an expanse of water, my sanity it saves,
Moving the sail to port, beam reach,
I instantly pick up pace.

Sailing the waters of the open sea,
Is the only place I feel truly free.

Sonny Palmer (13)
St Thomas More High School For Boys, Westcliff-On-Sea

THE SOVIET UNION

It began in 1917
And ended in 1991.
What was it?
The Soviet Union.

They built the Berlin Wall
And fought in the Cold War.
What was it?
The Soviet Union.

It had nine leaders,
From Lenin to Gorbachev.
What was it?
The Soviet Union.

The Americans built bombs,
But they built power plants.
What was it?
The Soviet Union.

They successfully built the first satellite
And called it Sputnik 1.
What was it?
The Soviet Union.

It began in 1917
And ended in 1991.

What was it?
The Soviet Union.

Sotirios Sotiras (15)
St Thomas More High School For Boys, Westcliff-On-Sea

CLIMBING THE FLAT MOUNTAIN OF BLACK AND WHITE

Throughout history, black and white have battled,
Divided in a game of chequered inequality.
The game of chess.

Throughout history, black and white have battled,
Attacking and defending for rights or squares.
The game of chess.

Throughout history, black and white have battled,
Yet still, society is divided in the greed and misconception of
checkmate.
The game of chess?

Yet really, is the game of chess really a game?
Or a sick view of our society?
Which should not be as so, but it is,
This isn't a game of chess.

M J Bowden (14)
St Thomas More High School For Boys, Westcliff-On-Sea

ISOLATION

His heart sank like a broken boat in the ocean,
But his face showed no emotion.
He stood still and frozen,
Like a statue, he was posing.

He smiled from ear to ear,
But inside, there was fear
His forehead soaked with sweat
Like a man filled with regret.

His legs were shaking,
Feeling like they were breaking.
His head down in shame,
Like getting shot with all the blame.

Red wrists,
Should he end it all with a twist?
Does he write a goodbye,
"All my love, I will be looking from up high."

Bartosz Szcech (14)
St Thomas More High School For Boys, Westcliff-On-Sea

THE ENGINE

Inlet valves sucked,
Cylinders flooded,
Pistons squeezed,
Spark plugs enflamed,
Crank shaft turned,
Wheels rotated.

Moving like a lift, inlet valves opened,
Filling with fuel, cylinders grabbed, drank and guzzled,
Pressing and compressing, pistons pressed, creating
pressure.
Spark plugs ignited an angry fire,
The crank shaft is the backbone of the robust engine,
Making movement.

Suck!
Squeeze!
Bang!
Pop!

Moving thunderously and never-ending.

Thomas Miller (14)
St Thomas More High School For Boys, Westcliff-On-Sea

UNTITLED

It's the buzzer beater,
Hit a triple-double.
I think I'm on a heater,
His ankles are broken.
The eyes that glare are frozen.
Dunk like DeRozan,
Or hoop like Emmerson,
Challenge him, he'll show you a lesson.

Wait a minute, it's time
To cook up and get in my groove.
Time is going, quick, I need to hurry
To drop twenty threes like I'm Chef Curry.
Be the king of the game,
Like I'm LeBron James,
Win play-offs, tip-offs and rebounds,
You can never win on these grounds!

Rio Abloh (14)
St Thomas More High School For Boys, Westcliff-On-Sea

A BIG CHANCE

The whistle is blown,
The referee points to the spot.
This is my moment,
My tummy is in knots.

It feels like slow-motion
As I walk to the goal,
The crowd roars loudly,
It shakes my soul.

I reach the spot,
The crowd goes silent.
Only on the inside
I feel very violent.

The referee blows his whistle again,
I take my run.
Will it go in?
Or be a disaster?

I kick the ball
With all my might,
The ball goes in.
The crowd shouts, "Night!"

Luke Bowden (12)
St Thomas More High School For Boys, Westcliff-On-Sea

INNOCENT PEOPLE

Crime right now is at its prime,
Meth just causes death.
They drive past so fast and guns ring like drums,
We have fears like innocent deer.
Innocent people go flying,
As buildings go crashing, lights are flashing,
Children are influenced by foolishness.

Wars are just like open doors,
Anything could happen.
We use tanks and flank to kill more,
People fight for rights, but we are all human.
We make mistakes which we soon regret,
The past is irreversible,
So you only have one shot.

Alfie Wilsmore (12)
St Thomas More High School For Boys, Westcliff-On-Sea

BREATHING

I am hot and sweating,
My whole body burning.
My lungs hardly breathing, breathing,
Just barely breathing, breathing.

My legs shaking, breaking,
Arms flailing, mouth wailing,
I could not stop running,
Or I wouldn't be breathing.

The shadows are coming,
Behind me, they keep chasing,
Their arms stretching,
With wicked grins laughing.

They start grabbing and punching
And start their daily bullying.

Ernest Aquino (13)
St Thomas More High School For Boys, Westcliff-On-Sea

BEACH IN ENGLAND

Your feet sit on a golden glow,
The heat you feel between your toes.
You lie down, relaxing aimlessly,
The bad weather has said goodbye.

The ball of fire is beaming down,
So now it's time to cool it down.
Take a dip in the ocean,
The bad weather has said goodbye.

The skies are turning angry and grey,
It's no longer going to be a good day.
Tears are starting to fall down,
The bad weather has said hello again.

Matthew Wills Vandervelden (14)
St Thomas More High School For Boys, Westcliff-On-Sea

IT COMES WHEN YOU NEED IT THE LEAST

It comes when you need it the least,
When it's gone, you'll fear it coming again.
It invades your heart and soul like a beast.

Until one person, a friend,
Inspires, a kind, humble person
Through kindness, lights your inner fire.

You cannot see or touch it,
But it will tear your soul apart,
In every part of life it fits.

But only when you are finished and complete
And have overcome it,
Can you sleep.

Jude Peach (13)
St Thomas More High School For Boys, Westcliff-On-Sea

YOUTH

Inspired by Carry On

Be a part of the latest trend
But, when is it all going to end?
Some friendships will never mend
But we can try to pretend.

Yawning in the morning,
Awake at night
Always acting tough
But we never have a fight.

Drinks are warm
And the weather is cold
Our clothes are torn
And the graffiti is bold.

Rotten to the core
Wrong side of the law
What on earth
Are you doing that for?

Tom Cozens (12)
St Thomas More High School For Boys, Westcliff-On-Sea

WORLD WAR

World War One has just begun,
Guns blazing, lives fading,
Buildings burning, smoke churning,
Poison gas fading in the wind.

World War Two is upon us now,
Missile shells are coming down.
Explosions to the left and right,
People's lives on the end of a thread.

World War Three seems far away,
But it could come on any day.
The world we know, the world today,
People's lives are about to change.

Connor Thomas John Lee (14)
St Thomas More High School For Boys, Westcliff-On-Sea

ONLY SOME

Problems, everyone has them,
Only some can deal with them

Talents, everyone has them,
Only some can use them

Opportunities, everyone gets them,
Only some take them.

We need to stop abusing society,
Live together in harmony,
Deal with problems as they come,
Use the talents that you've got,
You'll make it through,
Through it all,
The nights will be grim,
Which one are you?

Efeose Christopher Ukegheson (13)
St Thomas More High School For Boys, Westcliff-On-Sea

ACT

Our place in life may be small
And not enough for our population overall.

All these people we don't know,
But united, we should know

Respect, kindness and love,
For that is what our Father wants above.

But through these words we're speaking,
Are we really showing

As people, One's creation, our work should not be a burden?
So stand tall and be an example for the next generation.

Gio De Belen (14)

St Thomas More High School For Boys, Westcliff-On-Sea

IDENTITY

Identity is amazing,
Forever changing.
Those who are waiting,
Aren't ever chasing.

Those who give up,
Will never live up
To their expectations.

Identity is how you portray it,
How you convey it,
As someone may relay it.

However,
Identity is your friend,
Your family,
Your opinions,
Your memories.

Identity is who you are
And who you will be.

Joshua Naish (13)
St Thomas More High School For Boys, Westcliff-On-Sea

FRIENDS

Friends, who and what are they?
Friends, do they hate or like us?

Friends, are they fake or real?
Friends, will they leave us behind?

Friends, will they always be by my side?
Friends, are they the knowledge of our minds?

Friends, which one will go out with me tonight?
Friends, are they my path to happiness?

Or are they invisible to me?
Friends are the key to life.

Alfie Glover (13)
St Thomas More High School For Boys, Westcliff-On-Sea

EMOTIONS

Emotions start with trust.

Trust is like a key
To unlock love.

Love is a key
To unlock happiness.

Happiness is a key
To unlock surprises.

Surprises are a key
To unlock sadness.

Sadness is a key
To unlock evil.

Evil is a keyhole
That unlocks death.

Emotions end with death.

Aaron Antony (14)
St Thomas More High School For Boys, Westcliff-On-Sea

BULLYING

No matter what people say to you,
Don't let it get to you.
Go get a teacher or tell your friend too.

Go tell on him,
It isn't a sin
And get rid of the bad feelings from within.

I think, why is he bullying me?
Is it because I'm
tall,
cool,
fat
or small?
But now, because of him,
I hate school.

Zak Crisp (13)
St Thomas More High School For Boys, Westcliff-On-Sea

VICTORY

I'm breathing so hard
The others are gaining on us
Catching yard by yard

I pull on the oar
Until I can give no more
Hands and back so sore

Waves pour over the boat
From the bow sweeping to stern
Will we stay afloat?

The crowd cheers as one
One hundred yards to go
The gun fires, we won.

William Peck (13)
St Thomas More High School For Boys, Westcliff-On-Sea

EVERYONE'S DIFFERENT

Inspire others to change the world,
Go and help each other in a big whirl.

Sit down and pray for joy,
Now go and help that little boy.

Independence can boost your thoughts,
Using life just like we were taught.

Everyone's different,
But your life is yours.

Charlie Mchugh (14)
St Thomas More High School For Boys, Westcliff-On-Sea

LIFE

It's over now,
Now I have regrets,
Now I'm loved.

You're only loved once you're dead, rich or ill,
That's sad.
What if you aren't dead, rich or ill?

Everything is calm and still,
Like the ocean.
Time is ticking and your time is coming.

Korede Obayanju-Oladoyinbo (14)
St Thomas More High School For Boys, Westcliff-On-Sea

LIFE

Life is so short,
So live it to the fullest.
Don't ever look back,
But, keep striving forwards.

Life is precious,
You only have one.
If you love life,
It will love you back.
So, make sure you stay on the right track.

Vinay John Anthony Soares (13)
St Thomas More High School For Boys, Westcliff-On-Sea

LIFE

Life is living,
Not waiting,
Always making.

Life is loving,
Not doubting,
Always caring.

Life is wanting,
Not bearing,
Always sharing.

Life is what you make it.

Harrison James Baker (13)
St Thomas More High School For Boys, Westcliff-On-Sea

JOIN HANDS TO STOP RACISM

We are all God's creations,
Created to love and be loved.
White or black doesn't matter,
Muslim or Christian doesn't matter.
Let's be together,
Let's love each other,
Let's marry each other,
Let's care for each other
And always be there for each other.
We can make this world better for everyone.
No matter what colour,
No matter what religion,
We are all equal.
Live as one
And let love spread everywhere,
Join hands and stop racism.

Touleen Elawi (14)
The Ellen Wilkinson School For Girls, Acton

A TRAIN OF DESPERATION

Trapped in a wrecked cell,
It wasn't her body, it wasn't her soul.
Her head kept reasoning
But she knew she was breaking.
The cell was an illusion of thoughts,
Bounded by a nearly impossible freedom.
She turned an image of potential,
Into fear that she would crumble.

Her life was a train of desperation
And her thoughts were a constellation.
A process so dissimilar,
A series of distractions.
She knew she was a train off her track,
A river off her course.

Najah Harir (16)
The Ellen Wilkinson School For Girls, Acton

CHASING STARS

I have always looked up at the skies
And reached my hands,
To try to catch the stars.
But, the more I reach,
The more stars go further away.
I keep trying to catch them,
Until I can catch them.

Your future and dreams are like stars
And you are the chaser,
Chasing after them.
The more you try to catch them,
The more you will go on to success.
Don't give up and keep chasing stars,
Then, one day, the stars will shine in your hands.

Son Gyong Kim (14)
The Ellen Wilkinson School For Girls, Acton

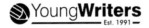
YoungWriters
Est. 1991

YOUNG WRITERS
INFORMATION

We hope you have enjoyed reading this book – and that you will continue to in the coming years.

If you're a young writer who enjoys reading and creative writing, or the parent of an enthusiastic poet or story writer, do visit our website **www.youngwriters.co.uk**. Here you will find free competitions, workshops and games, as well as recommended reads, a poetry glossary and our blog.

If you would like to order further copies of this book, or any of our other titles, then please give us a call or visit **www.youngwriters.co.uk**.

Young Writers
Remus House
Coltsfoot Drive
Peterborough
PE2 9BF
(01733) 890066
info@youngwriters.co.uk

 @YoungWritersUK    @YoungWritersCW